Leo
the Lion Cub

Story by Beverley Randell
Illustrations by Julian Bruère

Leo belonged to a large family of lions,
called a pride.
When he was only six weeks old,
his mother died,
so his aunts took care of him.

Leo was the youngest
and smallest cub in the pride.
All of his cousins were bigger
than he was.
They often knocked him over
when they played with him.
They liked pouncing on his tail
and biting it.

Leo had to be brave.
He had to learn how to fight.

Soon it was time
for the pride to move on.
The lions needed to find
a new hunting ground.

They padded off
through the dry grass,
one after the other.

But Leo could not keep up.
His little legs were too short.

When Leo whimpered,
one of his aunts stopped.
He tried to catch up with her,
but he could not walk fast enough.
So she moved on without him.

He was soon left behind.
He had never been alone before,
and he was afraid.

When the sun went down,
the night was full
of strange noises.

Leo heard some hyenas
howling in the distance.

He knew he must
keep out of danger.
He climbed a little way up a tree
and crawled along a branch.

The dark night seemed very long.

The next day, Leo saw a lioness
walking through the long grass!
But when he ran to join her,
he found that he did not know her.
This lioness was a stranger
who growled fiercely at him.

Leo could see her huge jaws
and her sharp teeth.
He was terrified.

Instead of trying to run away,
Leo rolled onto his back.
That was his way of saying,
Don't hurt me!
I'm only a small cub!

Leo was lucky.
The lioness turned away
and left him alone.

Leo had to spend
a second lonely night in a tree.

When morning came, he walked about
without knowing where he was going.
Soon black storm clouds
made the sky darker and darker.

Then lightning flashed
and thunder roared.
Heavy rain came pouring down.
The storm went on for hours.

Leo crouched under a low bush all night,
but he could not keep dry.

The next morning,
Leo looked half-drowned.

He was too young to hunt for food.
It had been three days
since his last meal.
If he did not find his family soon,
he would die.

Suddenly, Leo heard a lion
roaring in the distance.
He knew that roar!
Now he knew where the pride was,
and he set off again.

Leo struggled on through the wet grass.
He was very tired,
but he was not going to give up now!

And, at last,
Leo reached his family.
He was so glad to find them!
His aunts licked him all over
and fed him.

Then he lay down beside them
and slept... and slept... and slept.